GW00537674

Piano
Grade 7

Pieces & Exercises
for Trinity College London examinations

2012-2014

Published by
Trinity College London

Registered Office:
4th floor, 89 Albert Embankment
London SE1 7TP UK

T +44 (0)20 7820 6100
F +44 (0)20 7820 6161
E music@trinitycollege.co.uk
www.trinitycollege.co.uk

Registered in the UK
Company no. 02683033
Charity no. 1014792

Courante

from English Suite no. 2 in A minor, BWV 807

Johann Sebastian Bach
(1685-1750)

Suggested realisations:

Bracketed spreads are optional.
Both repeats should be played in the examination.

Sonata in F

R. 87

Antonio Soler
(1729-1783)

Allegro [♩. = 58–69]

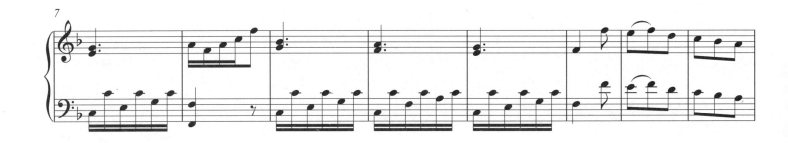

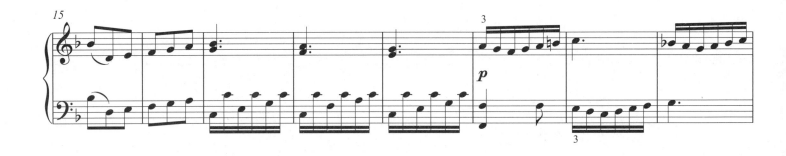

Dynamics and articulation are editorial.

6

Adagio and Allegro vivace

from *Caprice* op. 49

Johann Nepomuk Hummel
(1778-1837)

Song Without Words

op. 19b no. 1

Felix Mendelssohn
(1809-1847)

Assez lent

no. 2 from *Valses nobles et sentimentales*

Maurice Ravel
(1875-1937)

Assez lent - avec une expression intense [♩ = 96–112]

Composer's metronome mark ♩ = 104.

Assez modéré

no. 1 from *Trois mouvements perpétuels*

Francis Poulenc
(1899-1963)

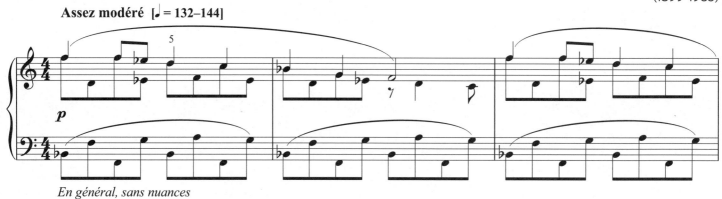

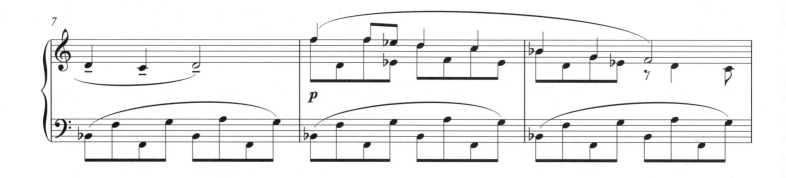

The repeat should be played in the examination.
Composer's metronome mark ♩ = **144**.

Sentimental Melody

Slow Dance (1929)

Aaron Copland
(1900-1990)

Ballade

no. 1 from *6 Pieces for Young Pianists*

Hans Werner Henze
(born 1926)

Composer's metronome mark ♩. = **42**.
Fingerings have been suggested for examination purposes only.

22

Melting

John Paynter
(1931-2010)

Composer's metronome mark ♩ = **60**.

Composer's note: The pedal markings must be strictly adhered to as the resulting
overtones serve to clarify the melting of the harmony and texture.

Exercises

1a. A Russian Song – tone, balance and voicing

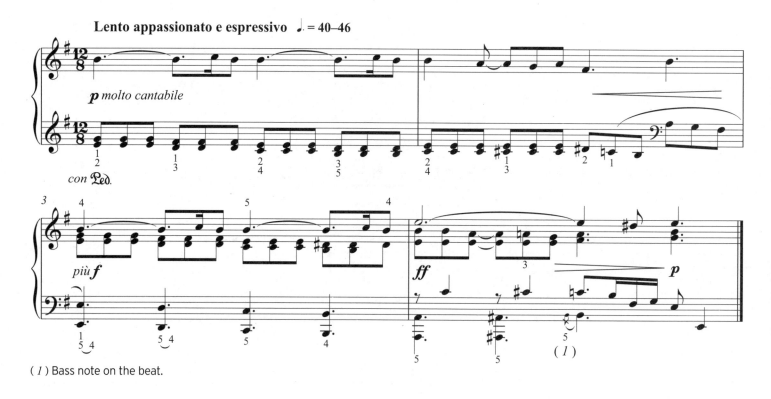

(1) Bass note on the beat.

1b. Song of Sadness – tone, balance and voicing

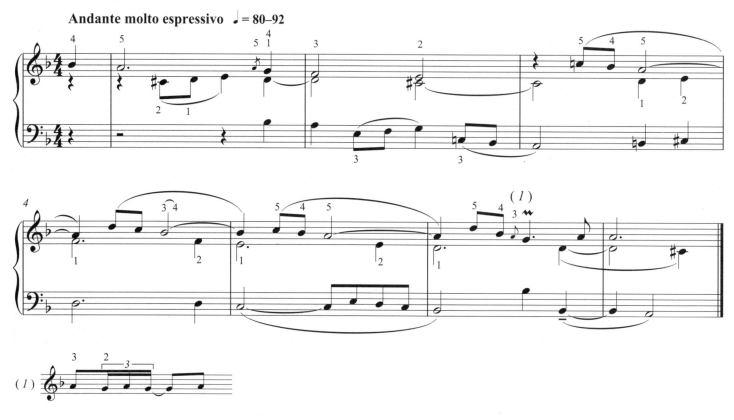

Dynamics have been left to the candidate's discretion.

2a. Basso sostenuto – co-ordination

Dynamics have been left to the candidate's discretion.

2b. Basso espressivo – co-ordination

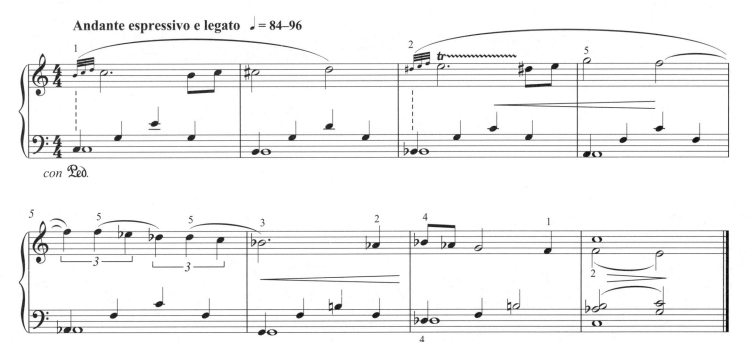

Dynamics have been left to the candidate's discretion.

3a. A Heavy Heart – finger & wrist strength and flexibility

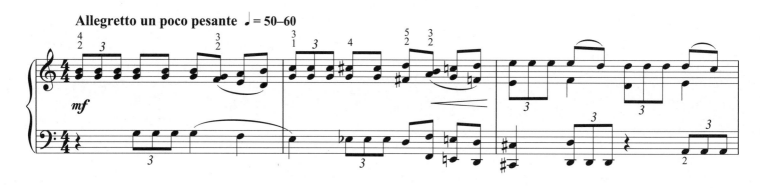

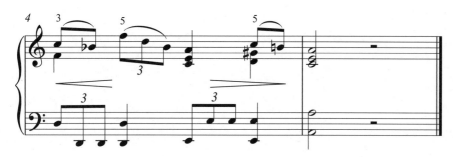

3b. Con bravura – finger & wrist strength and flexibility

Octaves in brackets are optional.

THE DORBOTT OF VACUO

For my daughter Rosie — audience, critic, friend — and
for all other Queeks everywhere.

THE DORBOTT OF VACUO

— or —

HOW TO LIVE WITH THE FLUXUS QUO

A TALE OF UTTERLY COSMIC INSIGNIFICANCE

by

PATRICK WOODROFFE

with a Foreword by Michael Heseltine

A DRAGON'S WORLD LTD. IMPRINT
Dragon's World Ltd.,
Limpsfield, Surrey RH8 0DY
Great Britain

ISBN Limpback   1 85028 047 9
ISBN Hardback   1 85028 046 0

Printed in Singapore

FOREWORD   by Michael Heseltine
Senior Expert Associate in charge of illustrated and children's books at Sotheby's of London.

I first encountered the Dorbott when Patrick Woodroffe showed me a series of drawings that he had made of the creatures and topography of a recently discovered planetary system, not too far removed from our own. He told me about the subject of each drawing in much the same way as someone describing a holiday through snaps taken while travelling abroad. As the drawings were not in any special order, I was introduced to the various weird and wonderful characters in a rather haphazard manner, but these descriptions were interspersed with other information which gradually pieced together to give me an outline of their strange history.

Patrick's enthusiasm and the fine detail of his drawings gave his descriptions an air of authenticity, and these hitherto unrecorded species were no less plausible than the cameleopards, mermaids, rocs and elephants reported by early travellers and explorers on our own planet. Here is the finished account with all the loose ends neatly tied up, complete with a well-researched analysis of ecological cause and effect which precipitated recent events in Vacuo. Although fully aware of the gravity of the situation, the author has nevertheless been able to introduce an appropriate degree of levity to the text, and this humour extends into his excellent delineation of the inhabitants and occurrences in this little universe. The responsibility for producing this account could not have been placed in better hands.

...HOME OF THE
RÊVE DIRIGÉ...

CONTENTS

PROLOGUE   Page 7
Chapter 1: A Void to Avoid   9
       2: Terra Infirma   15
       3: Three Kinds of Sanity   23
       4: Trouble with Mud   33
       5: The Dorbott at Home   39
       6: Critical Mass   47
       7: Impact   59
       8: Dénouement   67
       9: Loose End   73

PROLOGUE

In Vacuo nothing may breathe but the Chimaera,
nothing may burn but an idea.

Imagine the lining of a thermos flask — a mirrored, double-walled container — but turned somehow inside-out, so that the universe we know, our Sun, our planets, our stars, were contained within that mirrored lining, and outside were another, totally different reality, with other Suns, other planets, other stars.

Then imagine you lived neither in our universe nor in that other reality — imagine that you lived in the coffee that the thermos flask kept hot — half way between one truth and another.

Vacuo is like that, an inter-existential green-belt pushed to the very edge of our physics, where the enforcers of the Natural Law simply run out of motivation. It is a group of small, inconsequential planetoids, abandoned to a strange (but somehow logical) quirk of truth-functional calculus, viz. — that in Vacuo all those things may come to pass that elsewhere may be regarded as fiction, as myth, or (worst of all) as escapist wish-fulfilment. Vacuo is the home of the *rêve dirigé*; it could be Paradise, Utopia or Shangri-la. It could just as easily be Hell. The fact that it is neither of these reflects neither credit nor blame on its authors, revealing rather that they lack the imagination to be either excessively virtuous or excessively wicked in their dreams.

The Dorbott lives in Vacuo, as do many other remarkable beasts. To be precise, the Dorbott (and most of his best friends) now resides on *Regulo 5*, one of the many bodies that constitute the so-called *Vacuous Cluster*. With his languid body comfortably immersed in the marbled billows of the Great Swamp, the Dorbott is bizarre, the Dorbott is astonishing. Not only is he the most intelligent creature *in Vacuo* — remarkable enough in itself — but he also has a unique ability to remain utterly contented even in the most difficult circumstances. Events have often sorely tested his patience, as you will see.

The bubbling and heaving Swamp which the Dorbott frequents is also somewhat extraordinary. It is endowed with confused residues of intelligence and a vestigial self-awareness, and as you will see, such a thing is not unusual in *Corporesano* (another Vacuous planet — origin both of the Swamp and of the Dorbott) where so-called inanimate objects generally do have minds of their own. The Great Swamp consists not only of a dozen or so cubic miles of variegated mud, it is also a riot of intemperate entropy, a motley assemblage of lost goods, torn labels, long and short lengths of colour-coded string, broken chains etc., etc.

The Great Swamp is also contented — in its own somewhat limited way. Things haven't always gone well for the Swamp either, though most of its troubles might be said to have resulted from its own lack of discipline, its total disregard for the property of others.

No one has great expectations of a swamp. You're not expected to come up with original ideas or masterpieces of art. It would be a mistake to expect a swamp to do any real work. Most people are quite satisfied with your progress if you simply stay where you are and don't start wandering about messing things up.

On Regulo 5 both the Great Swamp and the Dorbott are honoured citizens, valued friends indeed of its ruler, the *Dustpan-Jandrum*. How this came to pass is an intricate web of narrative excess and gross literary tomfoolery, but then what would you expect? *In Vacuo* nothing may breathe but the Chimaera, nothing may burn but an idea.

Slipping lightly into the *passé historique*, we begin not at the beginning but somewhere near the middle.

... GROSS LITERARY TOMFOOLERY ...

ONE:
A VOID TO AVOID

We must go back many many years, to a time when things were very very different.

Corporesano was still a relatively unspoilt little resort, out of the way of most of the sophisticated goings-on in other planets of the system. It was a haven of contentment and peace compared for example with *Absentia*, the legal centre of the Vacuous Cluster, where the planetary economy depended solely on endless litigation. The crimes were blatant, the culprits obviously guilty, yet because no felon ever returned to the scene of his crime, no case could ever be resolved without complex extradition procedures.

Furthermore, Corporesano was a sanctuary of tolerance and liberalism when measured against *Locoparentis*, Absentia's nearest neighbour. On that pompous little world the Law was nothing more than a strong paternal hand, excessive in its zeal, righteous in its indignation, and even the most trifling peccadillo was punished with a sad severity — though always with the best possible intent.

Moreover Corporesano was very Heaven itself next to *Flagrantedelicto*, the most infamous place of all. That was where all the real criminals went to retire, forced to prey on their own kind, killing time in nervous luxury. In the end no one ever got away, for merely to apply for a visa to the place was considered sufficient admission of guilt.

It was only a matter of time, and one by one all the criminals were caught red-handed in Flagrantedelicto, tried willy-nilly in Absentia and punished for their own good in Locoparentis.

...THE CRIMES WERE BLATANT...

It was all rather sad, for the whole system had been a closed loop, an economic merry-go-round, and in the end, once all the back-log of cases had been dealt with, civilization (if you could call it that) ceased to function at all on any of these three worlds, and many discerning refugees fled the ensuing chaos to take up residence in Corporesano.

To them it seemed like an oasis of naïvety, a land blessed with child-like innocence and common sense. Of course it all depends upon the yardstick you use, for even the most liberal visitor might have found the place something of a shock.

The population of Corporesano — animal, vegetable and mineral — belonged to an extremely complex eco-system that had taken many millennia to evolve. A small apparent madness can sometimes be an integral part of a sane whole. So it was in Corporesano, where a biosphere had developed to fill a planetary niche where normal laws could never apply. Our hypothetical visitor, were he to condemn Corporesanian behaviour on the basis of his own ideas of normality, would make the mistake of ignoring the fact that ecological interdependence ultimately dictates all our behaviour — in Corporesano or on any other world.

Before the story can continue it is necessary to describe some of the historical and bio-chemical background, and to explain how the Dorbott and his Swamp fitted into all this.

..MARATHON-RUNNING WAS VIRTUALLY PANDEMIC...

Most Corporesanians were fond of P.E. Indeed a goodly proportion of the population were excessively concerned with the enhancement of their mental well-being by means of strenuous and all but continuous physical exercise. At the time of this narrative things were comparatively quiet, but there had once been a Dark Age when marathon-running was virtually pandemic and had given rise to a serious shortfall in the supply of foot-reodorizers. The consequences could have been catastrophic, but a careful conspiracy enabled the danger to be averted.

The properties of Corporesanian geology will be explained a little later on, but it is sufficient here to point out that it was a relatively simple matter for the authorities to make clandestine abbreviations to the marathon course simply by moving the finish closer to the start. The record was reduced progressively — eventually to such an absurd degree that even the most dim-witted runner realized that something was afoot. The craze subsided without further ado.

There had been other problems too. A fashion for aerobics had once reached such serious proportions that in order to restore and maintain a fair distribution of oxygen, the authorities had been forced to declare a planet-wide state of emergency. Special areas were set aside and designated *oxygenous zones*. Within their strictly-patrolled borders even press-ups were forbidden and the wardens were authorized to de-bag joggers on sight.

It seemed like tyranny, but on occasion it is necessary to take unpopular steps. Not that this move was unpopular with the entire population. Not all Corporesanians were enthusiastic athletes. Far from it. The less active members of society rejoiced in the peace and quiet afforded by these areas, and the lower life-forms proliferated undisturbed in the vast new *aeroblast* forests, where specially hybridized plants, genetically engineered to produce the greatest possible amount of oxygen, pumped out their restorative exhalations for twenty-four hours a day.

And various other measures also had to be taken to discourage hyper-activity, necessary interventions without which the entire population may well have been asphyxiated by its own CO_2, baked to a crisp by its own cumulative body-heat, or (worst of all) have suffered the agony of death by exposure to abnormally high levels of perspiration in the atmosphere.

... SPECIALLY HYBRIDIZED PLANTS...

TWO:
TERRA INFIRMA

There were exceptions, but as already indicated, this obsessive desire for movement often infected what an outsider might have taken for inanimate objects. A stone might suddenly roll about of its own accord, letters (with or without the help of a postman) might (or might not) deliver themselves, and ''moving house'' had a meaning hitherto unknown on our world. The lighthouse might jog around the bay for half an hour before breakfast, which you might think would make a nonsense of the Ordnance Survey, not to mention mariners' charts. You would be right. In fact no such things existed on Corporesano at all, for not even the smallest thing, not even one square millimetre of territory, could be relied upon to remain stationary forever — if ever.

...THE LIGHT-HOUSE MIGHT JOG AROUND THE BAY...

Special precautions had been taken to anchor the oxygenous zones — that being a high priority — but apart from that, any maps, charts, plans or title-deeds would have been utterly meaningless. This is why it had been so easy to dupe the marathon-runners by shortening the courses.

To repeat, by the time they got to Vacuo, the spatial planners had just stopped caring. All was chaos, disorder, flux. Yet somehow its people had learned to live with it.

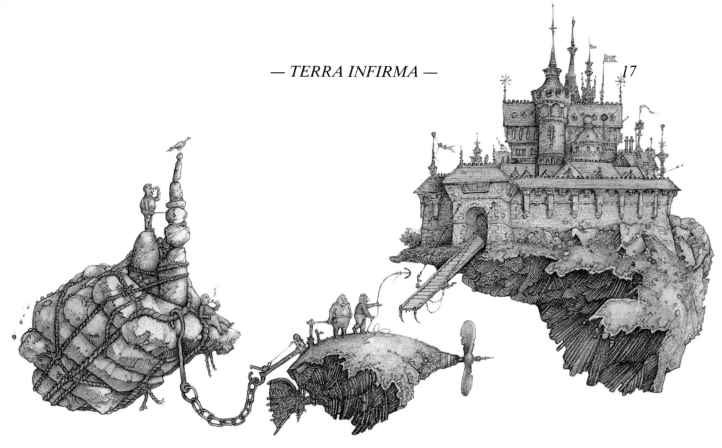

Huge tracts of land wandered about all over the place, like blimps or massive flying islands. This was just about tolerable, so long as they stayed the same way up and didn't suddenly tip over like melting ice-bergs. As in Einsteinian space, all these things moved in a way that could be described only in terms of each other. Relative positions were the only meaningful co-ordinates. The relationship of one moving object to those adjacent to it was of extreme social importance, and as in our world, relations would inevitably produce tensions.

And so it was that on the Dorbott's world the ceaseless metamorphosis of the landscape — sometimes subtle, sometimes violently obvious — was a topic of conversation even more popular than our earthly discussions of the weather. Instead of clouds they had wandering mountains. Instead of rain they had leaking lakes. Instead of hail-stones they had stones.

This effectively abolished politics, for there can be no politics without fixed territories to covet and defend. Not only that. It also had profound effects on the metaphysical and philosophical attitudes of the inhabitants. Just imagine. If similar uncertainties had played a part in the origins of the religions of our world — if for example the Sermon on the Mount had had to be postponed while the mountain went to visit Mahomet — then surely our own standards, indeed the very ethos of our cultures, would have been profoundly different.

What made it all much worse was the almost predictable perversity inherent in all this movement. In short, things always moved at the worst possible time. The clock might stop ticking to gain your attention, then circling its dial with both hands at once in opposite directions, would cock a snook at the very concept of time. Nothing was immune. Even the dining chairs, favouring colourful woollen leg-warmers, were liable to form a chorus-line at the drop of a hat. One could be sure that the table would remain utterly motionless until precisely four p.m. (by the delinquent clock at least) when one had just finished laying out the best china (all wire, Uhu and pot-menders) for afternoon tea. Hardly anyone played Scrabble any more; the tiles wilfully changed places all the time, coining unfunny and mostly rather lavatorial neologisms. Dominoes, jigsaw-puzzles and Monopoly went out of fashion the minute they were invented. And magnetism was no help at all, for even that phenomenon had been unable to come to grips with Corporesano. The poles took it in turns — ''sharing the lode'' they called it — alternately attracting and repelling.

...TEN TOTALLY MISCHIEVOUS COMMANDMENTS...

Come to think of it, this perverse magnetism may well have been the root of the whole problem. But anyway, nothing could be done; it was unendurable, yet nevertheless it had to be endured.

So, if the people of Corporesano seemed a trifle eccentric (even mad), we must make allowances. We mustn't judge too harshly in a world where circumstances were too tenuous to be extenuating for more than a moment, where at any time Ten totally mischievous Commandments were likely to come rolling down the mountain of their own accord, where the first stone didn't wait for him who was without sin before casting itself at anyone and everyone in random retribution. We mustn't condemn bad nerves, melancholia or agoraphobia in circumstances where we ourselves should undoubtedly have suffered the same maladies. In a world where temporary towns and evanescent villages drifted amorphously this way and that ...

. *AN ALTERNATING CURRENT OF TRUTH* . . .

where sign-posts tended to rotate slowly in the wind, as if powered (as it were) by an alternating current of truth ... in a world where a book might write (and read) itself ... where a coal-scuttle really did ... where a bread-bin could be a dangerous predator ... where an untethered pair of scissors might spend an hour or two happily snipping its way through the freshly-ironed laundry ... in such a world, is it surprising that the majority of the population were manic joggers, depressive weight-trainers, or (at the very least) paranoid alcoholics?

They suffered, yet did not fail. They were bent, nor yet did they break. Joining hands in mutual help, they ringed their foe with a disarming garland, placing a metaphorical daisy-chain — crown-like — upon the brow of outrageous fortune.

At least that was the theory. But all too often the chain would break, and some — like Diogenes — chose to seek their philosophies in the barrel or the bottle. Whither truth, they sighed, when even maths can change from day to day? And who would stay sober, when only drunkenness can make a crooked mile stay straight?

And so they went their different ways, born along not only by the planet's rotation — as we are — but by winds and tides as well. And such tides there were in the affairs of men that the ebb might leave them beached perhaps in sudden night, marooned (as it were) in endless day, or (worst of all) held captive in some ceaseless micro-climate of wandering rain and fog.

You had to keep an eye on the sky for fear of falling empties, the other on the

ground to avoid new pot-holes. You had to watch where you were going, even when standing still, *and* try to keep track of exactly where it was you had come from.

Imagine. Since birth you would have been forced to attach all your goods and chattels to something else — usually to your own person — if you wanted to be sure of ever seeing them again. Hence the huge importance of string in the Corporesanian economy.

In a wider context, many of the things which you and I take for granted did not exist in Corporesano at all, things which make up the foundations upon which our complex and comparatively stable society is based. There was no public transport (no reliable streets); there were no town-planners (no reliable maps); there were no daily milk deliveries (no reliable street-maps); there was neither radio nor television (perverse magnetism); there were no banks (no safe places for safes); there were no building societies (no mortgageable buildings) … and so it went on. All these things were unknown on Corporesano except in science-fiction stories so preposterous that no self-respecting author would be bothered to tether a typewriter to write them down.

Yet strangely enough herein lies the fundamental paradox of this remarkable world. Corporesano may have been a crazy place to be, with conditions guaranteed to reduce most men to despair, but nevertheless it was in Corporesano that lived the wisest beings in all of Vacuo — certainly wiser than most of us on Earth.

Not only is this largely accounted for by the absence of territorial squabbling of any sort and the physical impossibility of laying claim to any real possessions, but it was also underpinned by the absence of double-glazing salesmen, Sunday Newspapers, unsolicited mail, scratch 'n' win cards, apostrophe-en-apostrophes, Kentucky Fried Chicken packaging, space-invader machines, hovva-bovva ... and all the other manifold mixed blessings which make up the sublime yet burdensome heritage of twentieth-century Earth.

Somehow it seemed it was the very uncertainty of things, the basic instability of the planet, the *fluxus quo* itself that promoted these pockets of serenity in a turbulent world, for if one can once and for always come to terms with the essential mutability and perversity of matter, then I suppose one is — at least as far as anyone ever can be — sane.

...POCKETS OF SERENITY IN A TURBULENT WORLD...

THREE:
THREE KINDS OF SANITY

A more patient chronicler may well trouble himself with small gleanings, harvesting not the main crop of history, but picking along the edges of the field where the ground is flat from pounding plimsoll and iron pump. If those dumb bells could only speak! What changes in those far pavilions! What tales might be re-tolled by trophid cup and clapper?

Precious few, alas, precious few, and none that measure up for this story, which now must concentrate on those elements which had learned to be content, not only with their strange world, but also with their own stations in it — beings of sound mind and body, viz:-

        a) The Sealed Knot
        b) The Greased Garter
        c) The Carpediemite Tendency

The Dorbott belonged to the *Integumenta* (a sub-division of the *Carpediemites*) and to understand both his habits and his habitat, you should know something about each sub-division of these groups, always bearing in mind that these categories serve only to classify by occupation, allegiance and discipline, and do not imply any physical similarities, whether innate or acquired.

Those girdled by *The Sealed Knot* were drawn from an enormously diverse range of creatures, united only by a common devotion to their chosen activity, some winged, some many-legged — all variously furred, feathered, scaled or shelled. There were three sub-divisions — the Ligamenti, the Pigmenti and the Mementi.

The *Ligamenti* were primarily concerned with the manufacture, distribution, reclamation and re-cycling of the vast quantities of string, rope and chain needed to maintain a minimum tolerable degree of fixity in an inherently unfixed environment. It was the Ligamenti who had established the oxygenous zones, tied them in place with thousands of reef-knots, sheep-shanks and clove hitches. They were the supreme altruists, conscientious to a fault, a well-disciplined pseudo-militia, a devoted environmentalist élite. The Ligamenti literally stopped the planet falling apart.

The *Pigmenti* were the universal labellers. By the thorough application of a complex but universally understood system of colour-coding, related items were (where possible) identified and to some extent kept track of during their unpredictable wanderings. Vast quantities of paint, labels and stickers were required for this undertaking, which in the league-table of Corporesanian industries came second only to the production of string. And as things slowly moved about and got lost, all the remnants of peeling paint and fading labels became a characteristic feature of the Corporesanian landscape — everywhere striped, flecked and spotted in sad remembrance of long-forgotten claims, counter-claims and vain attempts at empire-building.

The Dorbott's Swamp especially was a wondrous kaleidoscope of such marks and monograms — a potage of a myriad ingredients, a veritable minestrone of now unidentifiable flotsam and jetsam. It was the fluxus quo *par excellence*, physical proof that all the efforts of the Pigmenti were doomed to inevitable failure, and yet somehow — because of the mute testimony of all that muddled colour — it none the less remained a permanent monument to their diligence and perseverance.

...THE ALTRUISM OF PERIPATETIC
SPRING-INTERIOR FURNITURE...

The *Mementi* lived dangerously close to the edges of common sense. While the Ligamenti tied things down and the Pigmenti labelled them, it was the chosen task of the Mementi to log and record — as far as was useful or salutary — the various movements of all significant properties. Their problem arose, as one might expect, from the difficulty of determining before the event which of the myriad movements might in the end prove to have been of significance or interest. The drop-out rate among the hard-pressed Mementi would understandably have been very high, had it not been for the altruism of peripatetic spring-interior furniture, which tended to follow them around whenever they looked like doing something rash. As a rule however, the Mementi were so selflessly devoted to their duties that their minds were very sharply concentrated. It was only during rare lapses of concentration that they perceived the awesome futility of their task and so succumbed to despair.

Adherents to the second major group — *the Worshipful Order of the Greased Garter* — were devoted to the welfare of plants, to the maintenance of a useful ecosphere based upon the foundations provided by their colleagues of the Sealed Knot. In fact without the Knot, the Garter would have fallen.

They were like Voltaire's Candide and his companions, having decided that in an unstable and fundamentally perverse world, the best thing to do is just to "keep beggaring on", to muddle through, and most of all to get on with the gardening. This group was also thrice sub-divided, into the Greens and Royals, the Garter Kings of Arms and the Knights Orderly.

The *Greens and Royals* planted, propagated, pruned, pollinated and in all other necessary ways assisted the proliferation of the aeroblasts, the oxygenous vegetation. By way of sobriquet they were also known as the *Greens and Pleasants*, and sometimes (because of their manner of hopping from branch to branch) as the *Spring Greens*.

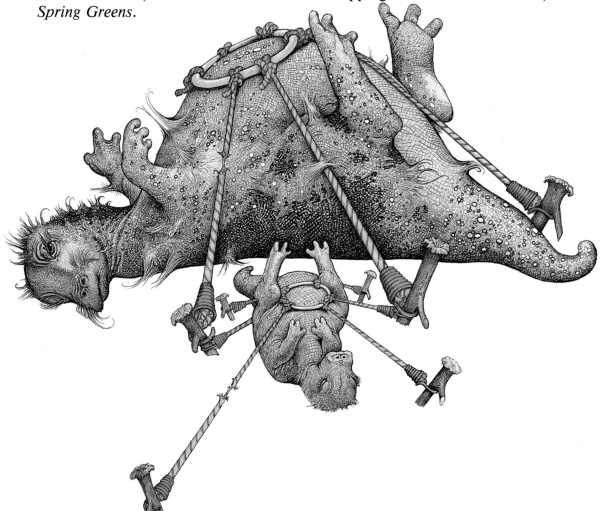

...SOME OF WHICH REACHED
GARGANTUAN PROPORTIONS...

Next came the *Garter Kings of Arms*, the nearest thing there was to a Corporesanian constabulary. Equipped with multifarious gadgetry, they were charged with the protection of the plantations from unwelcome browsing ruminants, some of which reached gargantuan proportions, or from the manifold tinier pests which might attack the precious aeroblasts by way of root, stem or branch. Hence the title "Greased Garter", which described one of the commoner expedients whereby creepy-crawlies were prevented from climbing up their legs as they worked. The Garter Kings were by nature however soft-hearted to a degree incompatible with their prefectorial function. They didn't hold with severe punishment, neither corporal nor capital. Persuasion was their usual *modus operandi*, and failing that (which meant nearly always) the ultimate sanction was deportation. Voracious snails, burrowing beetles and crop-crunching pachyderms were all treated with equally damp-eyed firmness and impartiality. Whatever their race, creed or dimensions, all creatures harmful to the aeroblasts were transported by air-ship to the other side of the world and dumped among less civilized and usually unappreciative antipodeans.

A Garter King bore in his left hand the *reticule*, consisting of a plastic bucket with a non-return valve in the lid to receive slugs, snails, etc. for deportment. In his right hand he wielded the *stick-with-a-nail-in-the-end*, the only weapon he was allowed with which to persuade larger creatures to accompany him to the station.

The final sub-division of the Greased Garter were the *Knights Orderly* — gentle heavyweights, big of bone, small of brain, patient and diligent work-horses. It was their job to keep the place reasonably tidy by trimming the edges, weeding the paths and removing any stationary litter. They were also expected to "move on" such items as busking pipe-organs, itinerant semi-detached bungalows and volcanoes of no fixed address.

...VOLCANOES OF NO FIXED ADDRESS...

And now (at last) we come to the *Carpediemite Tendency*, the third great division — the class to which belonged the illustrious Dorbott and his ilk, those who had succeeded in turning the fluxus quo to their own advantage, those who had learned to live with it, even to love it. Once again there were three roughly defined sub-divisions — the Integumenta, the Figmenta and the Thoroughly Bogus.

The *Integumenta* were generally remarkable for their thick skins, large ears* and casual attitudes. They made much of not caring a fig for what anyone else did or thought about anything at all. To generalize unmercifully, the Integumenta were all hedonists and lotus-eaters, a pleasure-seeking underground that none the less

*Except for the Fuddigongs and the Queeks, of whom more later.

religiously eschewed any pleasures that demanded effort — like breakfast, or getting up before three in the afternoon. All were formidable small-hours dissenters, heroic chewers of the fat, and their love-affair with music was legendary, if somewhat one-sided.*

Second came the *Figmenta*, a multifarious band of remarkable monsters, hybrids, freaks, sports and Freudian slips. They had good reason for their blithe good humour, their unclouded bliss, for the Figmenta, springing suddenly in and out of existence according to the strange laws of Vacuous physics, were nothing more than the product of other people's imagination, the physical incarnation of day-dream, nightmare or deliberate lie. They had no control even of their smallest actions, which of course absolved them from all responsibility and guilt. They were content to remain amused observers of their own brief careers until such time as the dreamer awoke, the nightmare was broken or the romancer exposed. It was all great fun, and even the serious bits didn't hurt.

. . . NOTHING MORE THAN THE PRODUCT OF OTHER PEOPLE'S IMAGINATION . . .

*Except for the Fuddigongs and Queeks, for reasons to become obvious.

The third group, the *Thoroughly Bogus*, were the happiest and sanest of all. They had nothing to worry about at all because they simply didn't exist. Not existing had been proved by research to be by far the most effective way of keeping out of trouble. A gathering of more than one Bogus was, for obvious reasons, generally referred to as a "charm" of Bogi. Some people favoured the Bogi as pets, feeding them (for the sake of economy) on a mixture of dehydrated water and elbow-grease. On special occasions they might be given giraffe's eggs in turtle milk followed by their second favourite *bonne bouche* — breadfruit and yam sandwiches; however, eight out of ten Bogus owners whose pets expressed a preference said their Bogi liked nothing better.

One Bogus of note was black Blanche — a born mother — whose little daughter Melanie was said to be a born baby.

...A BORN BABY...

FOUR:
TROUBLE WITH MUD

The story proper will soon begin, but first you have to know a little more about the Great Swamp and its fascinating history.

All swamps are largely made of mud, and even in the most stable of all possible worlds they are a bit unpredictable and potentially rather undesirable neighbours. But in Corporesano, with its history of geo-magnetic instability, the Swamp Problem had waxed to mind-boggling proportions. The Ligamenti had despaired of ever being able to tie it down. No matter how much string they used — it was no good — the loathsome stuff just kept slipping through. And the Pigmenti fared little better. Painting and labelling errant clods of semi-liquid gunge can be both frustrating and time-consuming. Even the level-headed Mementi lost hope of ever keeping track of the phenomenon; they took one look and threw in the towel.

... THE LIGAMENTI HAD DESPAIRED ...

As it turned out it was lateral thinking that won the day. Of low rank, yet none the less renowned among the Ligamenti, was Private Drawstring, who incidentally was also Grand Master of the Corporesanian Morris-Men. He kept his head cool and his spirit level. He addressed the problem as if it were one of poor discipline at rehearsals, where a sliding scale of punitive press-ups was in operation.

Do not forget that the Great Swamp had a modicum of intelligence, confused and vestigial though it was. To stay still would have meant intolerable boredom, so this huge volume of sentient slime insisted on hiking aimlessly about the planet in random lumps — messing up peoples' back gardens, vandalising public property and agglomerating more and more disparate paraphernalia in its glutinous mass. It was the weightiest walker the world had ever seen — in fact the only pedestrian that has ever been capable of running over a motor-car. It seemed unstoppable.

... THE ONLY PEDESTRIAN THAT HAS EVER BEEN
CAPABLE OF RUNNING OVER A MOTOR-CAR...

Now, as already mentioned, Drawstring was a lateral thinker. He knew that the Swamp had a mind as well as matter, and approaching the problem anthropomorphically, decided to persuade the Swamp to pull itself together. This wouldn't do at all, he pointed out, thrusting a huge ear-trumpet into the mire, all this indiscipline, all this anti-social debauchery. What the Swamp needed was a good healthy fitness programme.

The idea was to persuade the Swamp to tire itself out by excessive exercise, and then, when it lay exhausted in an unsuspecting swoon, to weigh it down with a few obliging Integumenta, who were only too willing to lend their weight to such a project, it being the first time they had ever been called upon to do anything useful that involved no effort whatsoever.

The plan actually succeeded. For the foreseeable future the Great Swamp seemed securely anchored. What is more, most of the rather bulky Integumenta were now out of the way and happily accommodated in a new and interesting habitat, which at first seemed to suit them extremely well. Everyone else was now free at last to cope with all the lesser vicissitudes of life in a mischievous world.

Even the Great Swamp seemed grudgingly satisfied in his new situation. It shared a much more stimulating social life — at least from mid-afternoon to the early hours. Now safely tethered, it heaved and swelled in token recalcitrance, tamely pulsating with an almost musical rhythm, and concealing (as it transpired) the eponymous hero of this book, the most lovable of all the Integumenta, the amazing solitary Dorbott, Warden of the Mud (which he adored), Keeper of the Keys (which he had lost) and Master of the Rolls (which now lay buried under the Swamp).

As already indicated, the Dorbott was remarkably intelligent, a fact wordlessly demonstrated as he lay snoozing in the midst of the Swamp, unassailed by any desire for action, luxuriating in the knowledge of the utter appropriateness of his physical attributes for the habitat in which he had volunteered to reside. He would lie submerged for whole days at a time, only his nostrils and ears protruding above the slime. And thus, if need be, he could remain forever, his filter-like beak taking nourishment directly from the ooze, his nostrils extracting life-giving oxygen from the air that wafted past, and his remarkable ears — most important of all — missing not one single hemi-demi-semi-quaver of whatever oratorio his gramophone might broadcast to him and his equally music-loving neighbours.

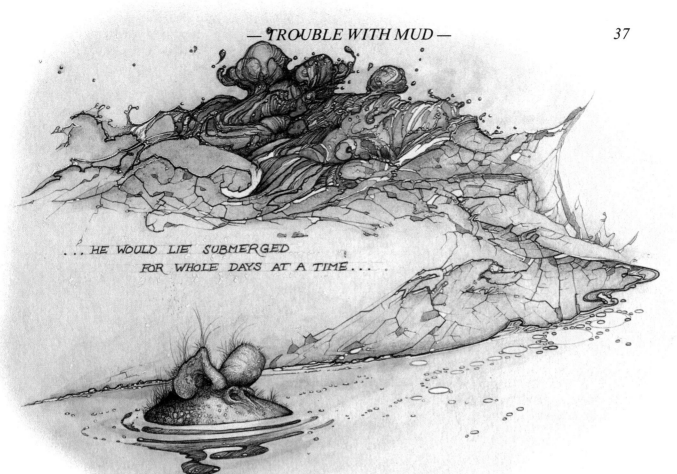

...HE WOULD LIE SUBMERGED
FOR WHOLE DAYS AT A TIME...

For his ears, like those of all Integumenta*, were extraordinarily efficient organs. In fact his hearing was so acute that he could (had he wished) have registered the tiny grunts of a germinating seed or the sussuration of little flowers when some far-off meadow flexed its petals in synchronous morning callisthenics. Indeed any idle tittle-tattle might have betrayed itself willy-nilly, had not the Dorbott chosen to ignore the majority of his in-coming stimuli and to concentrate (when not listening to music) solely on gossip that concerned him directly. However, given his uninviting habitat and his almost solitary life-style, such chatter was rare to the point of virtual non-existence, which meant that the Dorbott — though he heard all things — listened to very little and remembered nothing at all. He had the highest potential intelligence of any creature in Vacuo, but he stubbornly refused to pay attention. He happened to prefer it when his mind was a blank.

...HE HAPPENED TO PREFER IT
WHEN HIS MIND WAS A BLANK...

*Except Fuddigongs and Queeks.

... *HE LOVED TO TRY TO TIDY UP THE SWAMP* ...

This freed his brain to observe the world about him. He would spend hours watching the mud shrinking and cracking in the sun, or slowly liquefying again when some wandering river-valley passed overhead, blotted out the light and cooled the Swamp with a fine spray of peaty highland water.

He was quite content to sit up all night watching the Moons not being at all totally eclipsed. He was not given to conceits nor to portentous pronouncements. Like most Integumenta, he preferred to pleasure his senses rather than exercise his mind. He was happy because his pleasures were cheap and simple. He loved to try to tidy up the Swamp, revelling in the idiotic futility of it. When the weather was wet, he would spend the whole day mud-sliding. When he wasn't in the mood for music from his gramophone, there was nothing he liked better than absolute silence. He could listen to it for hours.

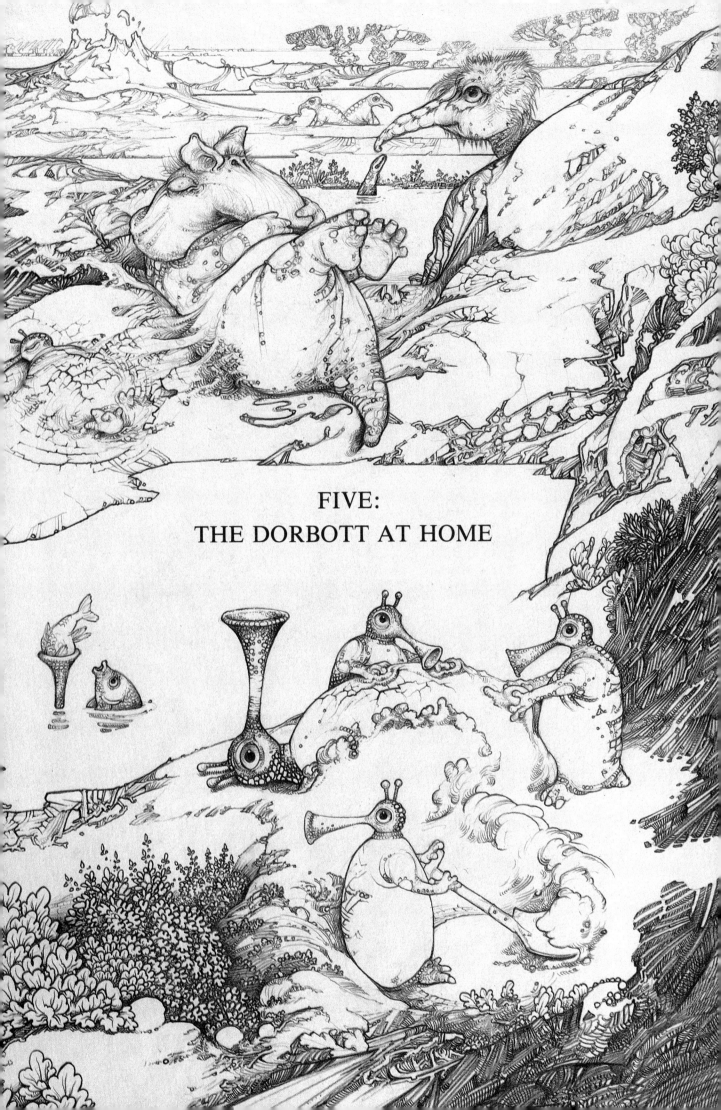

FIVE:
THE DORBOTT AT HOME

In this love of peace and quiet the Dorbott was however something of an exception. Most of the Integumenta in fact had rather noisy habits. Not only did their devotion to music overload the neighbourhood with a conflicting barrage of disparate melody, but recently many of them spent an increasing proportion of the all-too-short day complaining about the Swamp, themselves or just life in general.

The *Grigglebix* for example never stopped eating. This wasn't because he was greedy, nor even because he liked food. He was neither *gourmand* nor *gourmet*. He simply considered himself too thin, though in truth he was obese to the point of obscenity, and when not loudly bemoaning this erroneous self-image — posing disconsolately before a monstrously wide-angle mirror — he was usually to be found amid a vast midden of comestibles, hoping to munch and gulp his way to a more pleasing physique. The Grigglebix was intensely boring. He was not content to keep his self-absorption to himself, and constantly assailed his friends (those few he still had) with a commentary on his progress and requests for reassurance that he wasn't — Heaven forfend — losing any of those vital inches. Who will rid me of this turbulent beast? — said the Dorbott to himself.

... THE SQUOOCHLIK SHOULD NEVER HAVE COME ...

And then there was the *Squoochlik,* aesthete *par excellence,* whose critical pronouncements on literature and affairs of the art were so extremely well-tuned and perceptive that they seemed to obviate all need for the arts themselves and many regarded him as a second Ruskin. The Squoochlik should never have come to the Swamp in the first place. The essential amorphousness of it upset his aesthetic sensibilities to such an extent that he continually railed against its lack of form. For the Dorbott these railings made a prison and all the other bores a cage.

Worse still was the *Gurglibeek,* master of the insane practical joke, small of brain and loud of laugh, constantly planting stink-bombs, placing phoney newspaper adverts under other peoples' names and disguising his voice over the telephone. Now the Dorbott was an enthusiastic cat-napper, and the Gurglibeek's most recent wheeze was to dream up as many methods as possible by which to surprise the Dorbott into unwelcome wakefulness. A sense of humour was one thing; this went much too far.

...TO SURPRISE THE DORBOTT INTO UNWELCOME WAKEFULNESS...

Worst of all were the *Queeks* — a whole tribe of them — specialist half-bakers of philosophy (H.B.P's) who would spend the long hours of darkness in acrimonious dispute about for example the speed of thought, the persistence of memory and whether or not those unfortunate automobile passengers buried under the Great Swamp may have been mercifully rein*car*nated elsewhere, perhaps in some entirely different vehicle. The Queeks would have driven even Albert Schweitzer to misanthropic berserkerism.

This was the state of affairs when the narrative starts to pick up speed. The Dorbott was beside himself with annoyance. Things hadn't always been like this. When the Integumenta first settled in the Great Swamp, community relations had been extremely good, but now ... Perhaps it was the comparative over-crowding, the imposed ethnic mix. Anyway, something would have to be done, thought the Dorbott, to restore to his life the pleasant repose of yore. He initiated a careful eradication programme to rid himself of his tormentors.

To liquidate the Grigglebix was easy. A simple strategy of unkind remarks about anorexia nervosa — the occasional use of bald insults like "skull-face" and "bean-pole" — soon succeeded in reducing him to tears. From there it was simple. The tears were quite easily mixed in with the mud and served to enhance its liquidity. A little desultory tidying away of his food débris removed all evidence that the Grigglebix had ever existed. The Dorbott kept the mirror though; it proved to be a most effective hiding-place when people wanted him to do something. So fascinated did the visitor become by his own grossly distorted reflection that he tended not to think of looking for the Dorbott concealed behind it.

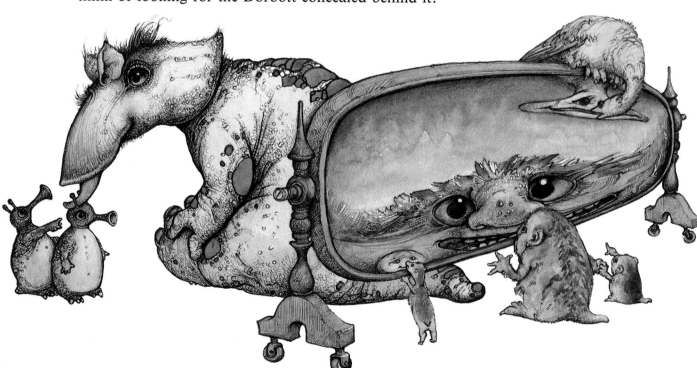

The Squoochlik presented even less of a problem. He had stayed this long only from a sense of devotion to duty, and now he had succumbed to a complaint common among the artistic: he had lost all integrity. The Dorbott loaded all the bits he could find onto a big hand-cart, and, whetting his friend's appetite with vivid descriptions of primitive tribal art, persuaded him to embark immediately on a passing dirigible. This one happened to be bound for the antipodes, loaded with a cargo of yogis who had been convicted of performing abdominal breathing in a restricted area.

The Gurglibeek seemed a little more difficult. But then the Dorbott had the bright idea of lending him a library-book entitled *"Making Your Own Pétard and How to Hoist it"*. In a matter of hours the Gurglibeek re-emerged to try his latest trick and went completely to pieces when it succeeded.

...HIS LATEST TRICK...

So now only the Queeks remained, stubbornly refusing to move at all, having decided that the whole affair had become a matter of principle. Whatever the Dorbott said by way of threat or persuasion, he got nowhere until he hit upon the ruse of pretending to have changed his mind. With counterfeit tears and a histrionic wringing of his hands, he begged them on his knees to stay with him always, and the Queeks, perfidious to the end, decided they would have to leave after all, having remembered a totally spurious previous engagement to immerse themselves in a think-tank at a forthcoming science-fiction convention. They packed their bags forthwith, and with a final toot of simulated regret, took themselves off to seek a promised land where their brand of original thought would be more highly valued.

...THE WHOLE AFFAIR HAD BECOME A MATTER OF PRINCIPLE...

And so it was that the Grigglebix, the Squoochlik, the Gurglibeek, the Queeks — in fact all Swamp-dwelling Integumentoids of whom the Dorbott did not approve — were soon either cleverly eliminated or deviously banished to another eco-system, leaving the Dorbott in sole* occupation of the Great Swamp. He erected a fence around his private domain, and here and there notices were posted bearing such legends as:-

"PRIVATE — KEEP OUT",
"INTRUDERS BY APPOINTMENT ONLY" and
"TRESPASSERS WOULD BE BORED TO DEATH".

Now this was all very well — the Dorbott at least was content — but his unilateral declaration of an A.C.R.O.N.Y.M. (Area Controlled by the Restrictive Ordinance: Not Your Mud) contributed much to a calamitous chain of events which the poor creature could not possibly have foreseen.

A little further background study is again required here in order to understand the situation. At last we come to the *Fuddigongs*. The Great Swamp was in fact not an exclusive Dorbott Reserve at all. The Fuddigongs (a most numerous population) had been allowed to stay because of their quiet and mild manners. These gentle ungulates had similar habits to those of the Dorbott himself, though — having no ears at all — didn't even know that music existed and were not in command of the Dorbott's awesome talents.

*Except for the Fuddigongs.

Up to this point in history the Fuddigongs had led a most carefree life, being mentioned only in foot-notes*, and because of their deafness had not even been troubled by the Squoochlik &c. who had so disturbed the Dorbott. They were free to play about in the mud all day with nothing to do but shave.

Yes, the shaving was something of a drawback. Stubble insisted on recurring at least four times a day all over their heads and faces, and to neglect one's depilatory toilette was to run the risk of being trapped in a thicket of suffocating locks. But this was a small price to pay for the pleasures of being a Fuddigong, and their lives otherwise seemed destined to remain an eternal idyll of muck-fights, tig-chase and mud-pie competitions.

...A SMALL PRICE TO PAY FOR THE PLEASURES OF BEING A FUDDIGONG...

*Like this one.

A Fuddigong had another unusual feature which was crucial (as it turned out) not only to this story but also to the entire history of the Vacuous System. Its back was attractively crimped like the crust of a Cornish pasty — that thick doughy crescent by which the tin-miners of old were said to hold it, and which was in fact not eaten for fear of the poisonous minerals that might be ingested from their unwashed hands. The importance of this will become clear very shortly.

So, just to recapitulate briefly on the global situation: the planetoid of Corporesano contentedly ploughed its orbital furrow, its various citizens enjoying the comparative stability of life now that the Great Swamp had been firmly anchored by the considerable bulk of the various Integumenta. Now, as explained earlier, many of the latter had recently been banished by the Dorbott, and in fact this fragile stability now depended entirely on those teeming Fuddigongs, whose combined weight was all that remained to keep the Great Swamp in place. Remove the Fuddigongs and all Hell would break loose — which is in fact what happened, though to reveal that fact here is to commit a stylistic error diminishing the impact of exact chronology or *strict tempo*.

However, be that as it may — back now to the situation as it obtained on that fateful day when the first real villain of this drama exposed itself beneath the proscenium arch.

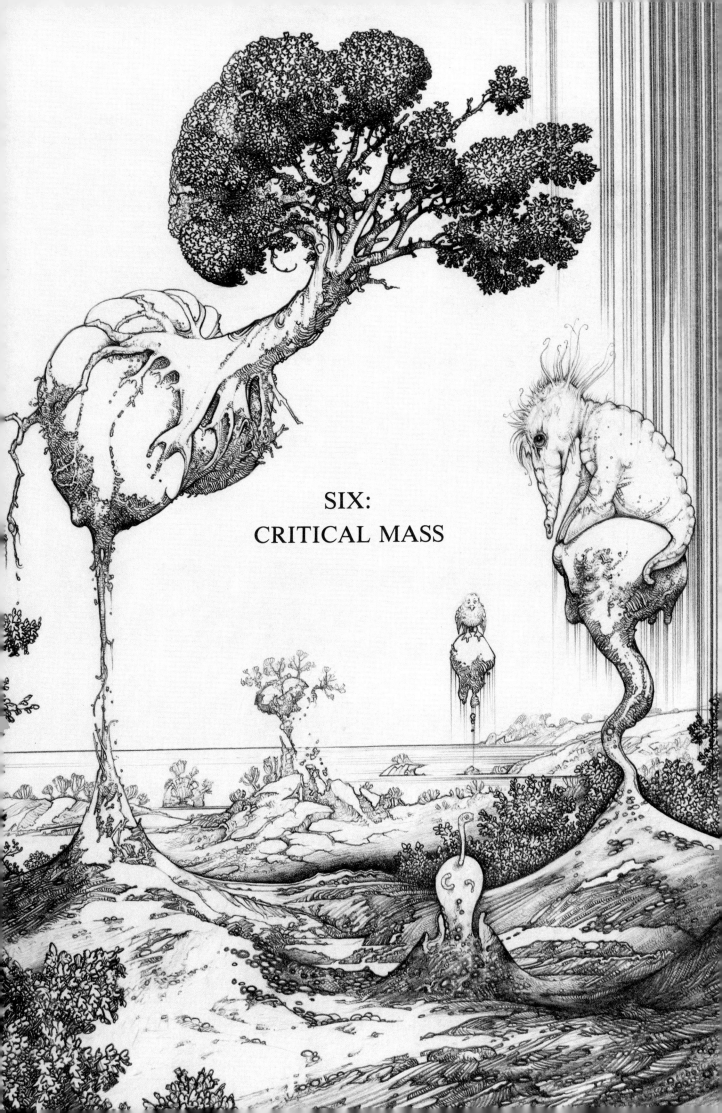

SIX:
CRITICAL MASS

Not far from the Great Swamp — at least at that precise point in time — was the Great Desert, a massive assemblage of rhythmically contorted magma, frozen lava-flows, shifting sand, etc., that flew languidly through the air as if the island of Lanzarote had managed to withdraw its stony roots and had taken itself off on the Grand Tour.

It was a magnificent sight, rocking almost imperceptibly this way and that when buffeted by rising and falling air-currents. The sun gleamed on its jutting crystalline peaks, where ancient events lay encoded in shuffled rifts and buckled strata. It was an area of desolation as yet unredeemed by Greased Garter missionaries, indeed that stolid fraternity had for once admitted defeat. In fact nothing would grow at all in the Great Desert, and vast hectares of coloured sand drifted idly back and forth across its valleys and plains until some day it was wafted over the edge and fell like merciless rain upon the place beneath.

Until recently the Desert had floated like a permanent weather-system in a clockwise vortex of air that circled an equatorial sea. The broad, slow-moving shadow protected the sea from excessive evaporation, and as if in gratitude the teeming fisheries in its fecund shadow provided unlimited nourishment for the only inhabitants of the Great Desert — the gigantic *Orthopteryx* birds.

As the name may indicate, these remarkable though somewhat unlovely creatures were famous for their acute vision and their uncanny ability to navigate at night. These talents were undoubtedly essential to their survival, for after the day's fishing the flocks of Orthopteryx must quickly return to their wandering home in order to roost. For an Orthopteryx has very limited stamina when flying, and more importantly, is totally unwilling to learn to swim. Failure to find its home would mean certain death by drowning.

It is believed (by scientists who have studied the phenomenon) that this uncanny navigation is effected in some inscrutable manner by the bird's remarkable eyes, one of which (the left) is coloured red, while the other is green. Exactly how this works was never discovered, but an interesting freak of nature proved at least the existence of some such mechanism, for a mutation was once observed whose eyes were coloured in the opposite way. Instead of returning to the Desert in the customary anti-clockwise curve, this poor bird had to take the long way round, never arriving at the roost until all the other birds were ready to leave again. Mercifully, the poor creature suffered such stress and exhaustion that it died before it could bequeath its aberrant genes to another generation.

Everything seemed all right, but in fact this closed loop had been doomed from the very beginning. The chain of events was logical, inevitable, and (had one known the facts) predictable.

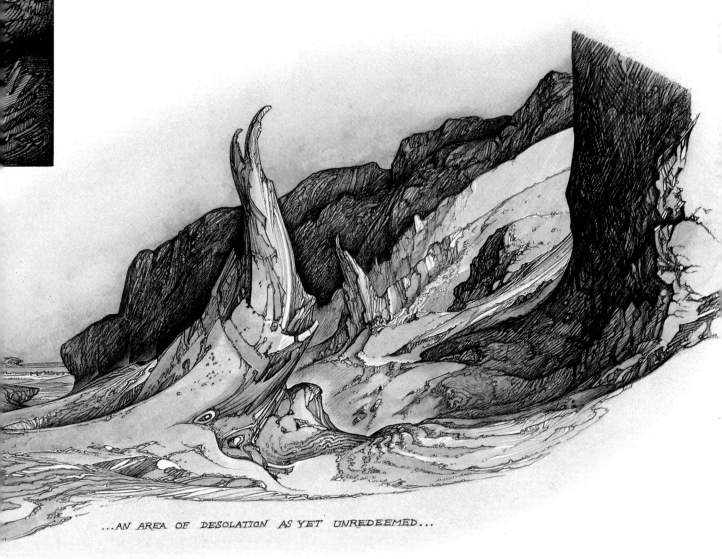

...AN AREA OF DESOLATION AS YET UNREDEEMED...

As the years passed by, more and more sand cascaded from the weathering peaks, spilling into the sea in a more or less continuous shower. In turn the sea-bed slowly rose, causing the waters to spread ever more widely over the land. The evaporation rate of course increased accordingly, aided by the ever-decreasing proportion of the sea protected by the Desert shade.

Inevitably the equatorial sea eventually dried up, the Orthopteryx birds had nothing to eat, the stationary vortex of air ceased to be stationary, and the Great Desert wandered up into the northern latitudes, its rocky ramparts manned by an unbroken fringe of starving birds, their red and green eyes eagerly scanning the passing landscape for signs of nourishment, a gastrocentric horde desperately seeking alternative creatures to predate.

There was only one stationary weather-system in the northern hemisphere that was large enough to capture the wandering desert, and that was the continual rotary motion of damp and foetid miasmas that encircled the Great Swamp. It was inevitable, pre-ordained by immutable physical law, that the one should find the other and that they should hit it off immediately like teenagers in love. The vast peaks of the Great Desert marched above the mud like a conquering army, the huge parasol of wandering rock suddenly shading the Swamp, the Dorbott and the Fuddigongs beneath a vast mixed metaphor. This generated a system of falling air-currents, which in turn caused the once-errant desert to be locked ever more firmly in position, though soon adopting the confined clockwise motion it had exhibited back home on the Equator.

... SEEKING ALTERNATIVE CREATURES TO PREDATE ...

The Swamp, involuntarily expanding and contracting, quite enjoyed the astringent temperature-gradients, as did the Dorbott and the Fuddigongs, and everything might have settled down once more into a comfortable harmony, had it not been for the fact that the Orthopteryx birds, queueing impatiently along the desert edge, were still unfed.

The Dorbott didn't like the look of them at all, and buried himself in the mud to await developments, but the Fuddigongs, unfortunate beasts, were still entranced by the novelty of sand falling from the sky, and being deaf, were totally unprepared when the screaming flocks of Orthopteryx birds hurled themselves from the cliffs in a feathery cascade.

The Fuddigongs died by the thousand, poor things, though even when the Orthopteryx were all quite full, there were still a good many left — enough at least to provide an adequate breeding stock and the basis of a stable ecology. Things were bad for the Fuddigongs. There was no more playing about in the puddles, no more carefree mud-fights — just one long life-and-death game of hide-and-seek. The Dorbott knew he was helpless. He just stayed where he was, resolved to sleep it out.

It wasn't a very happy place any more, but at least the whole thing would have been a viable system, had not the Orthopteryx birds reverted to a revised version of one of their most ancient traditions. When they had lived down in the South Seas, it had been their custom to prettify their elaborate nests with the discarded scales of the fishes which they killed for food. They had vied with each other in an annual contest of decorative prowess, of aesthetic sensibility. The instinctive urge to embellish their nests must be satisfied in another way, and where fish-scales had been used in former days, the birds now began to festoon their young ones' nurseries with the various inedible remains of the poor dead Fuddigongs. Their little hooves might be tastefully arranged around the edge in tinker-tailor fashion, or their matted scalps might be plaited together in a lugubrious basket-work of bloodstained coiffure. The Fuddigongs no longer had time to shave, and those that had not already been eaten by the birds were having increasing trouble running away without constantly tripping over their hair.

As the weeks went by however, the fashion became very specific. It was that pasty-crust spine that attracted them, to be cemented in decorative courses by a liberal guano mortar. And before you condemn this behaviour as cruel and uncivilized, look first into your own nest and see whether or not you may have practised a not dissimilar custom — the framed butterfly on the mantelshelf for instance, or the cameo brooch, perhaps some beaded jardiniere for which a thousand tiny cowries gave up their little ghosts in a pot of boiling water.

And soon the horrible practice got completely out of hand, for the birds began to slaughter the Fuddigongs in huge numbers, so easy were they to catch, and although they ate as much as they could manage, they soon began (as it were) to throw away the pasty and keep the crust, vying with each other in bitter rivalries to build the highest, the widest or the most outrageously sculptural nest of all.

The consequences brought the threat of disaster for everyone — not least for the Orthopteryx birds themselves — for eventually, over a period of only a few weeks, the Fuddigong bio-mass was already approaching that critical point when the Great Swamp would once more be unleashed on an unsuspecting world.

Only the ever-vigilant Ligamenti had foreseen the danger, for they had been keeping an eye on the Great Desert anyway. In fact they had already begun an extensive anchorage programme, driving hundreds of huge screw-rings into the ground. As it happened they were fortunate enough to have sufficient time to put

...IT WAS THAT PASTY-CRUST SPINE THAT ATTRACTED THEM...

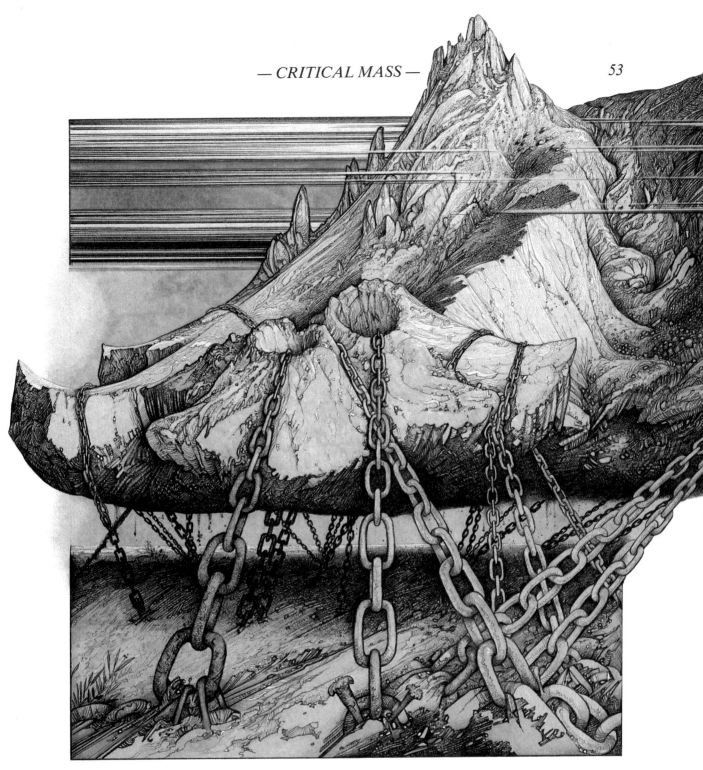

out a general Swamp Alert. Horns blew, klaxons sounded; there was panic everywhere. The populace had grown complacent of late, accustomed these days to comparative peace and security, and not surprisingly, they were extremely disturbed by the prospect of a resurgence of the mud problem. For the first time in history they were united by a common fear. The entire population made a massive concerted effort for victory. Soon all the Fuddigongs had gone — as sadly extinct as most of the more child-like and trusting creatures of our own planet — and the Great Swamp began to stir ominously like an animated rug, tentatively lifting a corner as if to test the wind in preparation for lift-off.

Unfortunately no one remembered to tell the Dorbott, who was of course submerged in the Swamp at the time listening to a vintage Muddy Waters album. Like the captain of a ship, he was destined to share the same fate as the Great Swamp itself.

Private Drawstring of the Ligamenti (he who had solved the problem last time) had fortunately just read a book all about mechanics, parallelograms of forces and so on, and once again it was he who came up with a stratagem that might save them all. Practically everyone was enrolled as special deputy, bearing the *carrick bend* insignia on a lapel button, and in a supremely orchestrated *prestissimo* of ligation, infibulation and concatenation, all movables* were tied down securely. Even the Great Desert was now firmly anchored. Progressively thicker chains had been threaded up through conveniently extinct fumaroles, and the whole thing was securely moored to the screw-rings which the diligent Ligamenti had already installed.

The plan required total cooperation, planet-wide determination, global discipline. This was the F.R.U.S.T. (*Fun-Run for Ultra-Spatial Swamp Transjection*), whereby at a pre-arranged signal the entire population — whether athletically inclined or not — would start to run in a westerly direction. Thus the total mass of moving bodies should have enough propulsive force (it had been calculated) to accelerate the rotation of the planet in the direction reactive to their movement. Then by centrifugal force the Great Swamp, being the only untethered item, would fly off at a tangent and be lost forever in the void.

---

*Except of course the Great Swamp — and, as it happened — the Dorbott.

.. WHETHER ATHLETICALLY INCLINED OR NOT ...

It worked.

The Swamp slipped away from beneath the Desert like a tablecloth decisively snatched from under the tea-things, and by way of a bonus, the Orthopteryx birds, being similarly untethered — and who incidentally were getting very hungry again and had been watching all these preparations with a confused suspicion — were flung off into the vast reaches of space to meet whatever fortune the Vacuous Fates might have in store for them.

The Desert, deprived of the meteorology that had kept it aloft, sank into the space vacated by the Swamp. Relaxing audibly, its contours gradually softened, it shrugged off a life-time of stress, resolved to turn over a new leaf and become a green and pleasant land. All the guano helped of course, and within weeks a gay carpet of aromatic flora had crept inexorably across the dunes, and sweet bird-song could be heard where just a short time before there had been only the raucous hubbub of Orthopteryx squabbling over the aesthetics of architecture.

Two (or more) ecological problems seemed to have been solved simultaneously, and for a while at least, all went well. Corporesano was blessed with the usufruct of a Golden Age. Society flourished and prospered in a way hitherto impossible. Now there could be order and stability as never before, and the old heroic diligence, forged to cope tenaciously in the former chaos, was now free to direct itself totally to more delicate civilized pursuits. That new unity of purpose, which had first revealed itself in the F.R.U.S.T., now quickly became a habit, and stable, cooperative behaviour contributed to an already well-advanced exponential rise in the standard of living.

But, you may ask, where did the Swamp end up? And whatever became of the Dorbott?

Somewhere in the silent backwaters of space, cruising along in total unawareness of his dangerous predicament, the Dorbott lay dormant within the Great Swamp, as its amorphous tendrils and tentacles were slowly moulded by its own gravity into a perfect sphere of damp débris. It sparkled prettily in the sunlight, the convoluted ebb and flow of its micro-tides displaying ever changing marblings of unreadable history. And eventually, like some errant missile in search of a target, the Great Swamp was drawn inexorably to the nearest gravitational field that lay in its path.

This in fact was the planet Regulo 5, which was mentioned briefly at the very beginning of this book. It was not a good idea to describe it at that juncture, for to do so would have diminished the impact with which it crashes into the story, or rather the impact with which the story crashes into it. Also, to describe the place in detail at such an early stage may have put you off the rest of the book and you may never have managed to get this far.

Regulo was the diametrical opposite of Corporesano. Like the iron balls on a sheet-metal press, they were destined never to meet, though their orbits were one and the same. Not only in space were they distant; the gulf was also an ideological one.

The undisputed ruler of Regulo for example was an aggressively tidy personage known as the Dustpan-Jandrum, who maintained a fanatically ordered régime of trans-fascist humourlessness and severity. Anyone displaying subversive tendencies towards sloppiness had long ago been eliminated, and the population of Regulo now consisted (to his considerable, though unsmiling satisfaction) exclusively of ruthless char-ladies, pitiless paper-spikers and cold-eyed housewives, a highly disciplined private army of obsessive pickers-up, compulsive sorters-out and manic putters-away.

. . . A HIGHLY DISCIPLINED PRIVATE ARMY . . .

The Dustpan-Jandrum surveyed the immaculate acres of his domain with a cold and joyless twitchiness, a strange insecurity born of suspicion. Could there be recidivism in the ranks? Far from rejoicing in the perpetual order and cleanliness that surrounded him on all sides, his keen eyes were alert only to the deviant, only to the indiscipline he dreaded. He'd got it all his own way, yet still could not be happy, for somehow he knew that such perfection couldn't last. How right he was.

Tall as a house, majestic of gait, he walked the shaven sward where the rare croquet tournament might sometimes be permitted — provided the tiny punctures in the lawn were filled in afterwards and no balls were allowed to dent the military precision of the herbaceous borders. That night he was even more nervous than usual. His red eyes gazed heavenward as if for reassurance, only to reveal to him the vast and tormenting chaos of space itself. The stars were so ill-managed, he thought to himself as he sadly scanned the twinkling firmament for some evidence of the orderly God in whose existence he so tenaciously believed.

After centuries of assiduous discipline a situation now obtained in Regulo which was the exact opposite of that which prevailed in Corporesano. Nothing was ever left lying around. Order had to be obeyed and always was. So obedient indeed were the Dustpan-Jandrum's subjects that, for fear of making a mess, nothing was ever done. Once the morning chores were out of the way, a mournful stillness fell, and nothing moved at all — all day — by order — by decree. If Corporesano could be regarded as the home of the *fluxus quo,* then in Regulo could be found a tangible manifestation of its antithesis, the *status quo.* In short, it was the dreariest place in the known universe.

The Dustpan-Jandrum turned away with a nervous frisson of dread. He wouldn't look at the sky any more that night, for he had just noticed with horror that one of the stars was moving, very fast, and seemed to be getting bigger.

So it was with the essential perversity of all matter that the Great Swamp of Corporesano — now a dangerous ball of mud racing through space without due care and attention — chose to wed its bulk to (of all places) the cleanest and neatest place of all.

The Great Swamp slowed down rather a lot when it struck the Regular atmosphere. First it orbited the planet a couple of times, as if deciding where and at what time of day it would be best to land. By now it had spread out again into an amorphous fluttering pancake, fragments detaching themselves delicately from the edges and making their own way down.

SEVEN:

IMPACT

One such independent lump descended in a tree not far from the summer-house where the Dustpan-Jandrum happened to be taking breakfast. Most of it fell perversely *outside* the litter-bin which had been provided as an assembly-point for the autumn leaves. With a snort of disgust the King of Regulo put down his tea-cup and went to investigate; this was no doubt the work of some over-eager apprentice over-loading his hover-barrow. But just as he stepped out onto the grass, a much larger bit of Swamp suddenly flattened the summer-house behind him, and all that remained of his breakfast was the one neat triangle of toast and marmalade he still held in his hand. And then a positively monstrous fragment, the nucleus of the Great Swamp, indeed the very locus of its feeble intelligence, decided that (all things considered) it liked the look of the Royal Palace best. It proceeded to exercise squatter's rights.

You couldn't watch. It was terrible. Mud everywhere. Filthy cushions. Dirt all the way up the stairs.

The Dustpan-Jandrum was furious. He rushed around his palace bleating with impotent wrath. He flapped his arms in crazed fury when he saw the mess in the sitting-room, tore his scales out by the roots when he saw the state of the bath-room, and when he finally made it to the garden — and saw the Great Swamp stretching out before him in acre upon acre of gloppy slime — something inside his head took industrial action. He suddenly went very quiet, then spent the whole of the night on a bare mountain.

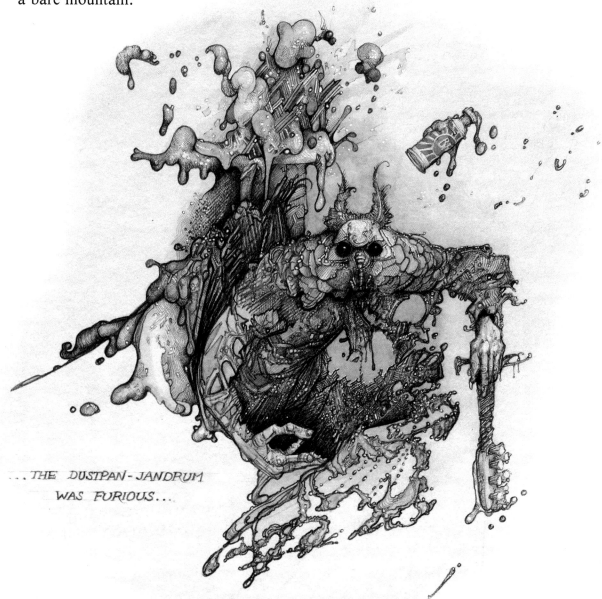

...THE DUSTPAN-JANDRUM
WAS FURIOUS...

It was this that wakened the Dorbott, who was very fond of Mussorgsky.

Next morning the Dustpan-Jandrum sat weeping in his muddied rockery, where hoards of thrift and precious banks of honesty now lay crushed beneath this unsolicited deposit from outer space. The Dorbott introduced himself and tried his best to cheer him up, though were he so inclined, he himself had sufficient cause for melancholia. The Dorbott, incapable of lying, told the tale as best he could, and the Dustpan-Jandrum, his red eyes betraying nothing of the plans that were forming in the brain behind them, listened attentively. Without recourse even to the mildest duress, he extracted the Dorbott's innocent betrayal. The Dustpan-Jandrum now knew where the Great Swamp had come from, and Corporesano lay naked to the greatest potential disaster that had threatened it for weeks — invasion.

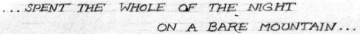

...SPENT THE WHOLE OF THE NIGHT ON A BARE MOUNTAIN...

It was useless to argue, for the Dustpan-Jandrum was adamant. He was determined forcibly to exchange one planet for another, to be granted what was morally his by way of compensation, and even the most hair-splitting legal brains concurred when Corporesano was tried in Absentia. The former king of Regulo 5 was unanimously proclaimed *Great Pretender* to the throne of Corporesano, and a formal treaty was drawn up by which all Vacuity undertook not to obstruct the Dustpan-Jandrum in any attempt he might make by *force majeur* to install himself king *de facto*.

The loyal populace of Regulo allowed themselves (to a man) to be wrought into a metaphorical iron fist, a flint-eyed monomanic war-machine. They stowed themselves and all their luggage in a formidable interplanetary armada, and one by one, on fiery pillars of smoke, great iron ships shot up out of the mud. Flying in a satisfyingly sagittate configuration, they slowly crossed the vast reaches of space that separated them from their rightful home, the new Jerusalem.

They passed a good many better worlds on the way incidentally — all of them uninhabited — but when you're going to a promised land there's always supposed to be someone there already, be they Red Indians, penguins or merely trees. Otherwise invasions aren't any fun.

... THE DORBOTT KEPT HIS PEACE ...

Meanwhile the Dorbott kept his peace, characteristically unconcerned. He guessed what would probably happen, and, content just to wait it out, returned to the Great Swamp (now of Regulo) to tidy up his record collection, which had been thrown into considerable disarray by the impact.

The dreadful invasion forces arrived one Sunday afternoon in November, on what may accurately be described as a "dead cabbage" day. A dull grey mist hung on the chilly air, a gentle drizzle bedewed the still trees, and the only sounds to be heard were the languorous re-folding of Sunday newspapers and the ineffably dispiriting flutter of flames in the parlour grate.

Corporesano had changed. No one ran any more — except to fat. It was boring. It was quiet. It was practically moribund.

A new and threatening over-stability had directly resulted from the solving of the Swamp problem. The Ligamenti had succeeded in getting everything tied up, right down to the last rod and perch, which meant that the Pigmenti and the Mementi had been made redundant. Some of the latter had even succeeded in doing away with themselves, for the upholstery that had saved them hitherto could no longer follow them around. So now even Corporesano had unemployment problems and suicide statistics, therefore qualifying as a thoroughly modern civilization.

It was in the parks that you noticed the changes most. Gone were all the gaily striped running shorts and the silky vests; all the former joggers, swaddled now in flannel combinations and tweed, lounged in well-moored deck-chairs perusing

commodity-market reports. The statues never batted a fig-leaf, the benches never dodged the descending *derriere* of the would-be sitter, the fountains never drenched the passers-by for innocent fun. It was as if the essential spirit of the place had been driven off by distillation, as if the dead hand of routine had strangled all the erstwhile zest for living.

Life may have been hard in the bad old days, but at least the man in the street was smiling when the window-box fell on his head. People used to laugh then, even though the joke always seemed to be on them. Marching along on the crest of a hill, keeping their eyes on the distant horizon, they would go down singing — blithely devoured by some new-born mine-shaft that spontaneously opened up at their feet.

But now the place had got to look almost as tidy as Regulo had done in *pre-Impact* days. In fact on that historic Sunday afternoon when the Great Pretender arrived with his cohorts of cleaners, he was agreeably surprised by everything he saw. All the mountains were arranged in neat rows, the woods were a very symphony of symmetry, the rivers ran as straight as rulers to a central sea as flat and as perfectly round as a crêpe-plaque. Even the smoke from the little thatched cottages rose up into the sky in perfectly parallel straight columns.

The new ruler was able to make a thorough inspection of his acquisition before any of its traditional inhabitants woke up from their afternoon snooze. He approved. In fact he was delighted, and without further ado dispatched his emissaries, legates and bailiffs to all the far corners of the globe to deliver specially printed but rather brusque invitations to leave.

It was a rude awakening, a bit of a cheek, a pretty kettle of fish — and on a Sunday too. The document got read, necks got red, noses got red, in fact an apoplectic rage of perfectly alarming redness seemed about to erupt, when all of a sudden, with no time for anger, no time for retaliation, yet another great historical *coup de théâtre* struck the planet.

SPECIALLY PRINTED BUT RATHER   BRUSQUE INVITATIONS TO LEAVE . .

EIGHT:
DÉNOUEMENT

... SHE KNEW IT MIGHT COME IN HANDY ...

It had begun harmlessly enough.

A Regular char-lady of low rank, yet endowed with a zeal above her station, happened to come across a small piece of string that just seemed to be lying about doing nothing. She knew it might come in handy, so she picked it up and began to roll it into a ball. However, she soon discovered a series of disagreeable knots which she conscientiously began to untie.

Soon they were all at it, frantically tugging and fiddling with every bit of string they could lay their hands on, seeming to compete in a race to see who could get the biggest ball of string before bed-time.

As it happened, no one was to go to bed at all that night.

All the string was of course the carefully managed corsetry that had been built up over the centuries by the labour of countless devoted Ligamenti. Without such stays and trussings the whole planet would crack up.

And so it did, though no one noticed until dusk. But by then it was too late. Telephone boxes and lamp-posts started to walk up and down the streets arm-in-arm, paving slabs detached themselves furtively from the carriageway, turning tentatively end-over-end until struck by unfortunate Sunday-afternoon motorists. A gasometer was briefly observed hovering dangerously close to a factory chimney ...

Before you could take it in — before some people even managed to change out of their slippers — a catastrophic domino-effect was underway. An imbalance in one area inevitably caused a dozen ruptures elsewhere, and this in turn led to further ruptures and imbalances, fanning out in an unstoppable *tsunami* of chaos that within hours had engulfed the whole world.

Civilization — in Corporesano still a novelty and a mixed blessing — was at an end.

For the second time in his life the Dustpan-Jandrum wept. Open-mouthed, speechless, aghast, that such chaos could be physically possible in a world created by a loving and All-tidy God, that such misfortune could strike so inopportunely the very planet he had just quite legally inherited as his own.

He ordered a muster to be sounded, though some never heard it above the din, and re-assembling his scattered legions as best he could, scrambled with them back to his iron ships. They teetered and slid about as the ground heaved and bucked beneath their flimsy pantographic legs, but soon they were back in space, retreating as fast as they had come. The Dustpan-Jandrum wasn't quite sure where to go next, but felt consoled to some degree at least by the knowledge that Regulo 5 — even with its newly-acquired Swamp — was a Paradise when compared with Corporesano.

So he decided to go back anyway, and in fact before the long journey was over, he had resigned himself to the inevitable, and decided to tolerate the Great Swamp after all. As a gesture of good will, he immediately invited the Dorbott to tea.

Perhaps, he decided, just a little mess here and there may be a good thing after all — it keeps you on your toes, gives a fellow an interest. He was soon forced to admit that his bad nerves seemed to have got better; he no longer worried about disorder, for now he knew there was no possibility of clearing it up. He began to enjoy life in a way he'd forgotten. He started listening to Schoenberg.

You might even have heard him humming, as he shovelled away the mud from his croquet-lawn. For the Dorbott and he were going to have a game, and after that they were going to tape each other's records. Soon they found they had a great deal in common and became the best of friends. They would often be seen strolling together beside the Swamp, either in a companionable silence or sometimes perhaps in friendly dispute about *musique concrète* or the rôle of atonality in the development of post-romantic free form.

Physical laws were different on Regulo 5. Things stayed put, including the Swamp. In fact it slowly ebbed from all the high places and coalesced in the lowlands in a pleasing imitation of a smooth though rather soupy ocean. Fashionable health-resorts, always an indicator of a healthy economy, sprang up along the shores, where the popular ailments of house-maid's knee, scrubber's elbow and polisher's palsy were now effectively treated by total immersion, hydrotherapy and mud-packs. Happy holiday-makers, released from the bondage of house-work by a retaliatory hobbling of the collective conscience, strolled up and down the new promenades, their bright parasols and pretty perambulators making a merry sunlit parade.

The Dustpan-Jandrum softened by the minute. He turned his palace into a children's home, his park into a fun-fair. He melted down most of his space armada to make clockwork trains and push-bikes. He even became a fan of the Springfields and decreed that everyone should call him Dusty. He was no longer the same person. He was unrecognizable. Regulo 5 was unrecognizable.

But so was Corporesano. The pendulum swings. The Swamp giveth and the Swamp taketh away. Corporesano had returned to the Dark Ages.

Yet curiously enough no one seemed to mind. In fact the very opposite seemed to be true. Most people seemed to prefer things that way.

The Ligamenti once more had a challenge to their ingenuity. The Pigmenti were back in work. So were the Mementi. In fact the more you thought about it, the more you realized how good things had been back in the bad old days before they got rid of the Great Swamp. There could be no more quiet evenings by the fire — the grate was liable to get up and walk away. There could be no more drowsy afternoons picnicking in the meadows — the land kept bucking and rolling like exuberant linoleum. It was goodbye to factories, a farewell to farms. Things were back to normal now. The *fluxus quo* was reinstated. It was anarchy. It was chaos.

It was great.

That sounds like the end, but it isn't.

NINE:

LOOSE END

The fabric of history is rarely a neat *macramé* of satisfactory conclusions.

Causality is continuous both in weft and warp, though marriage knot and funeral wreath may tie off episodic chunks along the way. If there are such things as temporal Ligamenti, then they shall never win. Time is a beast no man may tether. The most he may do is learn a careful husbandry.

In Corporesano nothing had really changed. Inevitably, by dint of hard work and ingenuity, things were bound to return to eventual equilibrium. The Great Swamp was still gone. A truly normal situation was unattainable. They were simply restoring the dreadful stability that had been prevalent immediately prior to the invasion from Regulo 5.

It was only a matter of months before they managed it, every Gordian knot re-tied, every errant girder re-girt, every label a fresh palimpsest exclaiming — *Sit! Stay! Mine!*

...*BACK IN THE BORING OLD GOLDEN AGE AGAIN*...

They were back in the boring old Golden Age again, sitting around reading colour supplements and eating too many chocolate biscuits. Everybody was under-worked, over-fed, fed up.

So, in the first interplanetary vehicle the Ligamenti had ever made, a special envoy was dispatched forthwith to Regulo to see whether the Dustpan-Jandrum was willing to have his Swamp removed.

Unfortunately he was not. In fact, as mentioned earlier, not only he, but all his subjects had grown very fond of it. Bog-beans and Marsh-Mallows were now the favourite foods. Wellington boots were the height of fashion. In fact the Swamp had applied an enormous fillip to the Regular economy. Industry prospered, work and leisure were comfortably balanced. The people were happy, and so was their King. So was the Dorbott, who would (like all the rest) have been most reluctant to forego his habitat.

. . . MOST RELUCTANT TO FOREGO HIS HABITAT . . .

The problem seemed insoluble. Not only that — it was absurd. Everyone suddenly needed the Great Swamp, when only months ago they had been trying their very best to get rid of it.

It seemed the case would have to go to litigation. In Absentia the lawyers rubbed their hands in anticipation of a complex and lucrative legal marathon. The Dustpan-Jandrum was legally King of Corporesano; therefore his antagonists were technically his subjects. The Swamp was legally the responsibility of Corporesano, the property of its rightful monarch. Had it been stolen? Was this a case of high treason *before the fact*? King Dusty (sic) felt ill. The Dorbott (sick) was off his food. No one relished the prospect of a trial.

Even the Swamp began to worry, so unaccustomed was it to so much attention. It went from bad to worse, from depression to mania, from paranoia to schizophrenia. It didn't have much of a mind to start with, but now it had two smaller ones.

If things would only stay like that for a moment, there was just the smallest chance of a compromise, an out-of-court settlement. The Dustpan-Jandrum was prepared to allow exactly fifty percent of the mud to be re-exported to Corporesano, provided there were regular cultural exchanges with the Dorbott's more interesting Carpediemite colleagues. Extra-Regular influences were now *de rigueur* in all fashionable circles. It was planned to import a few selected Figmenta to stimulate the Regular entertainment industry. The Dustpan-Jandrum even resolved to take a Bogus as a pet, as soon as one could be found that was house-trained.

...REMOVED BY A SMALL ARMY OF SKIPS...

Exactly one half of the Great Swamp, with exactly half its schizoid mind, was removed by a small army of skips and returned to Corporesano. So the Ligamenti once more had a satisfactorily indomitable adversary, which meant that an equilibrious *fluxus quo* was soon restored. There was once again a "dynamic shortfall" in string supplies, a symptom of an overall state of healthy insecurity, salutary unpredictability and astringent unrest. Causes had once more become challengingly estranged from their effects. And because no one ever quite knew what was going to happen next, they all lived happily ever after.

Or they would have done, had not this careless author left yet another loose end. For whatever became of all those Orthopteryx birds, ejected so unceremoniously into the void? Well, in fact the happy ending lasted only a few days — until a certain newsvendor (though warned by his employers) met a horrible and untimely death. He was the first victim of an epidemic of clairvoyance.

But that's another story.

THE END